Smash Hits

I CAN PLAY THAT! ™

Wise Publications
London/New York/Paris/Sydney/Copenhagen/Madrid/Tokyo

Exclusive Distributors:
Music Sales Limited
8/9 Frith Street, London W1D 3JB, England.
Music Sales Pty Limited
120 Rothschild Avenue, Rosebery, NSW 2018, Australia.

Order No. AM963237
ISBN 0-7119-8083-7
This book © Copyright 2000 by Wise Publications

Compiled by Nick Crispin
Music arranged by Stephen Duro
Music processed by Allegro Reproductions
Cover photograph: (Madonna) courtesy of LFI

Printed in the United Kingdom by
Printwise (Haverhill) Limited, Suffolk.

Your Guarantee of Quality

As publishers, we strive to produce every book to the highest commercial standards.
The music has been freshly engraved and the book has been carefully designed to minimise
awkward page turns and to make playing from it a real pleasure.
Particular care has been given to specifying acid-free, neutral-sized paper made from pulps
which have not been elemental chlorine bleached. This pulp is from farmed sustainable forests
and was produced with special regard for the environment.
Throughout, the printing and binding have been planned to ensure a sturdy, attractive publication
which should give years of enjoyment.
If your copy fails to meet our high standards, please inform us and we will gladly replace it.

Music Sales' complete catalogue describes thousands of titles and is available in full colour sections
by subject, direct from Music Sales Limited. Please state your areas of interest
and send a cheque/postal order for £1.50 for postage to:
Music Sales Limited, Newmarket Road, Bury St. Edmunds, Suffolk IP33 3YB.

www.musicsales.com

American Pie

Words & Music by Don McLean

Freely

A long long time a-go I can still re-mem-ber how the

mu-sic used to make me smile.___ And I knew that if I had my chance

I could make those peo-ple dance and may-be they'd be hap-py for a-

A tempo

while.

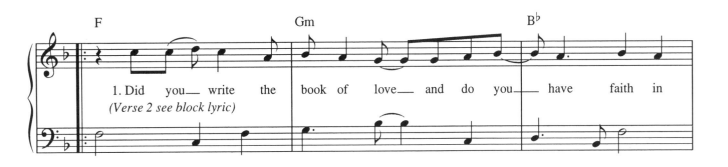

1. Did you— write the book of love— and do you— have faith in
(Verse 2 see block lyric)

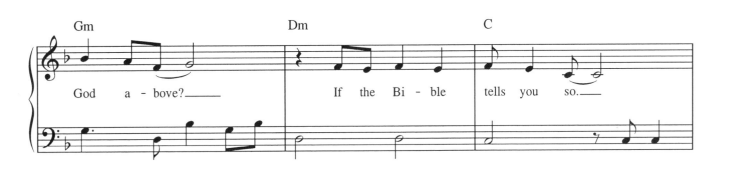

God a - bove?_____ If the Bi - ble tells you so._____

Now do you— be - lieve— in rock and roll— and can

mu - sic save your mor - tal soul, and can you teach— me

5

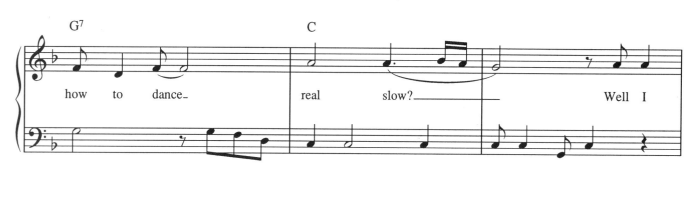

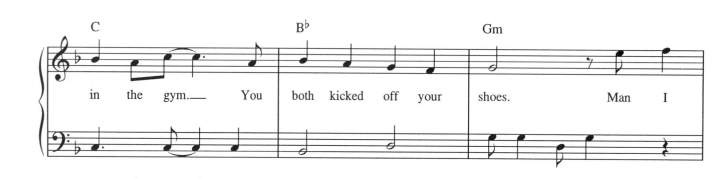

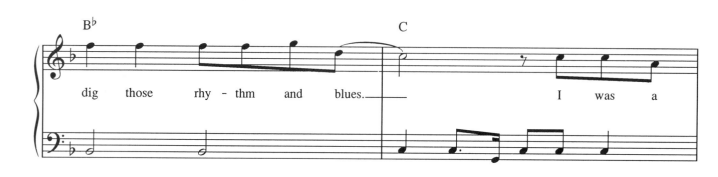

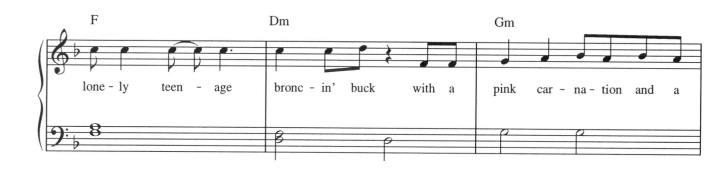

pick - up truck. But I knew that I was out of luck___ the

day the mus - ic died. I start- ed sing - ing

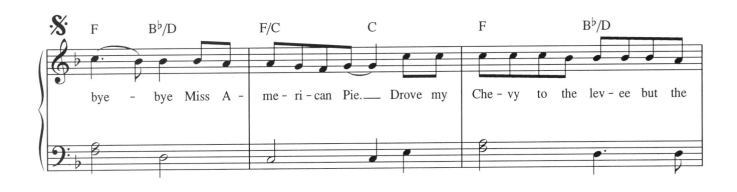

bye - bye Miss A - me - ri - can Pie.___ Drove my Che - vy to the lev - ee but the

lev - ee was dry. Them good ole___ boys___were drink - in' whis - ky and rye___ sing - in'

Dm · · · G · Dm · · · *To Coda* ⊕

This will be the day that I die.
This will be the day that I

1. C · F · C · F · C

die._____

2. C · *D.S. al Coda*

die._____

⊕ *CODA* C · F · C

die._____ We start-ed sing-ing._____

We start-ed sing-ing.____ We start-ed sing-ing.____

____ We start-ed sing-ing.____

Verse 2:

I met a girl who sang the blues
And I asked her for some happy news
But she just smiled and turned away
Well I went down to the sacred store
Where I'd heard the music years before
But the man there said the music wouldn't play
Well now in the streets the children screamed
The lovers cried and the poets dreamed
But not a word was spoken
The church bells all were broken
And the three men I admire the most
The Father, Son and the Holy Ghost
They caught the last train for the coast
The day the music died
We started singing.

Bye-bye Miss American Pie *etc.*

Breathless

Words & Music by R.J. Lange, Andrea Corr, Caroline Corr, Sharon Corr & Jim Corr

Moderately

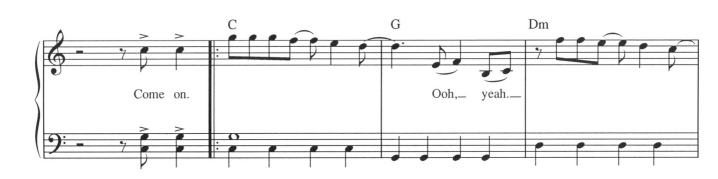

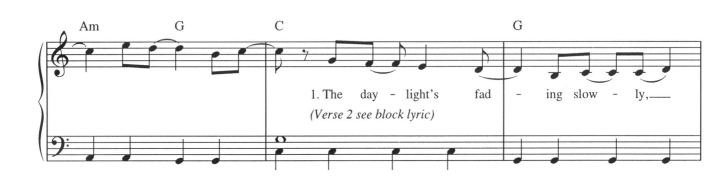

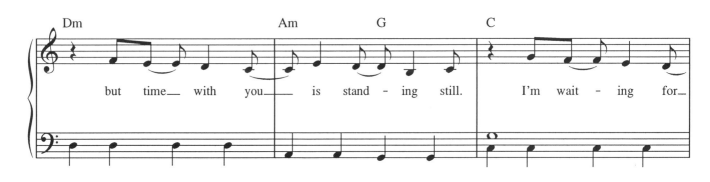

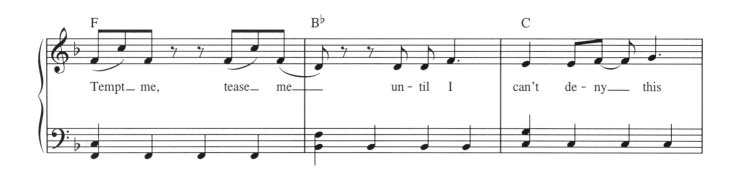

Tempt___ me, tease___ me___ un - til I can't de - ny___ this

lov - ing___ feel - ing.___ Make me long for your___ kiss.___

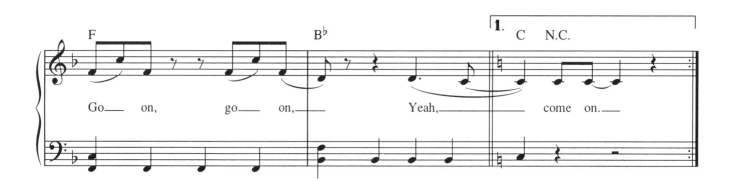

1.

Go___ on, go___ on,___ Yeah,___ come on.___

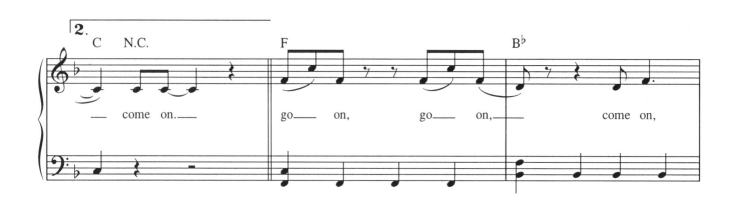

2.

___ come on.___ go___ on, go___ on,___ come on,

Verse 2:

And if there's no tomorrow
And all we have is here and now
I'm happy just to have you
You're all the love I need somehow
It's like a dream
Although I'm not asleep
And I never want to wake up
Don't lose it, don't leave it.

So go on, go on *etc.*

Against All Odds
(Take A Look At Me Now)

Words & Music by Phil Collins

Moderately slow

(M) 1. How can I just let you walk a-way, just let you leave with-out a trace? When

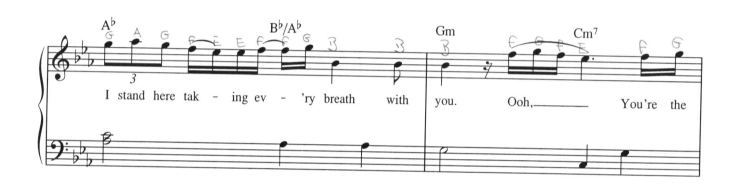

I stand here tak - ing ev - 'ry breath with you. Ooh,_____ You're the

on - ly one who real - ly knew me_ at all.

(F) 2. How can you just walk a-way from me_ when all I can do is watch you leave?_ 'Cos we've

(Verse 3 see block lyric)

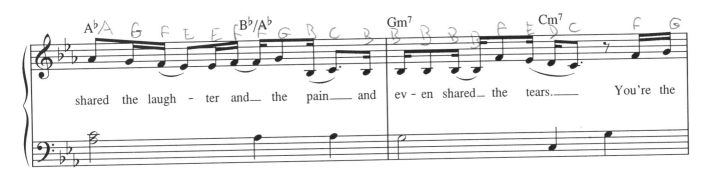

shared the laugh - ter and the pain and ev - en shared the tears. You're the

on - ly one who real - ly knew me at all. So take a look at me now,

'cos there's just an emp - ty space, There's no - thing

left here to re - mind me, just the mem -

-'ry of___ your face.___ Oh, take a look at me now,___

___ well there's just an emp-ty space.___ And you com-in' back___

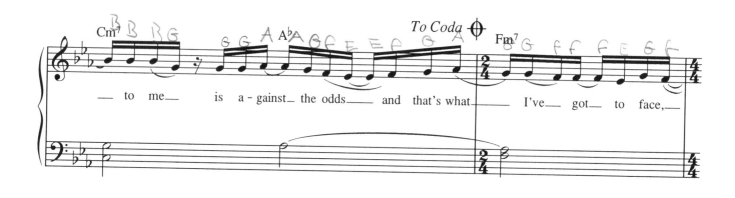

___ to me___ is a-gainst___ the odds___ and that's what___ I've___ got___ to face,___

(M) 3. I

— I've got to face. Take a good look at me now, _____ 'cos I'll__ still

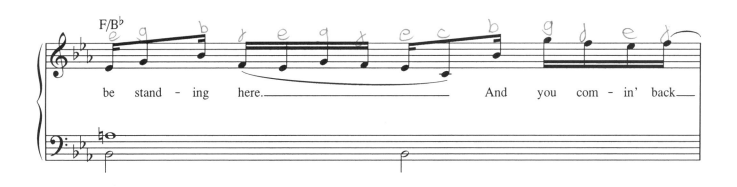

be stand - ing here. _____ And you com - in' back__

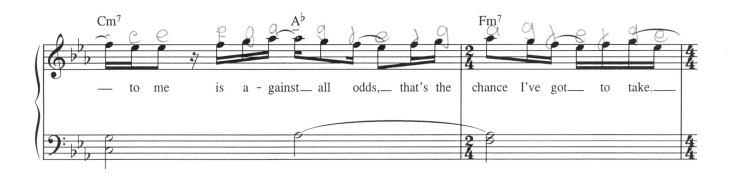

— to me is a - gainst__ all odds,__ that's the chance I've got__ to take.__

— (M) Chance I've got to take. Got to take. _____

17

Take a look at me now.— (F)Take a look at me now.—

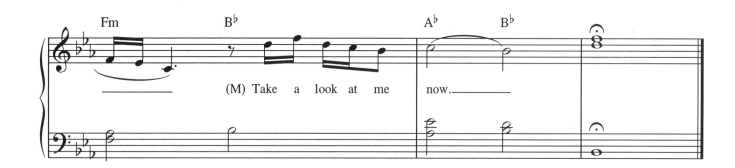

(M) Take a look at me now.———

Verse 3:

I wish I could just make you turn around
Turn around and see me cry
There's so much I need to say to you
So many reasons why
You're the only one
Who really knew me at all.

So take a look at me now,
Well there's just an empty space.
There's nothing left here to remind me,
Just the memory of your face.
Oh take a look at me now,
So there's just an empty space.
But to wait for you is all I can do,
And that's what I've got to face.

Fool Again

Words & Music by Jörgen Elofsson, Per Magnusson & David Kreuger

Moderately

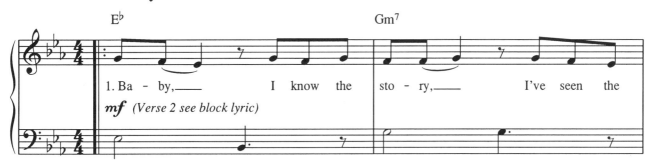

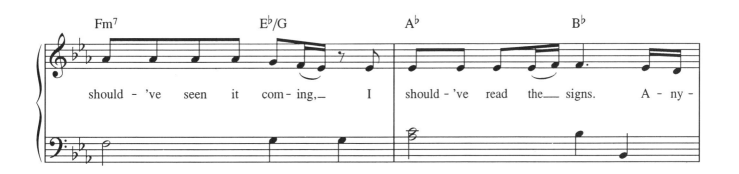

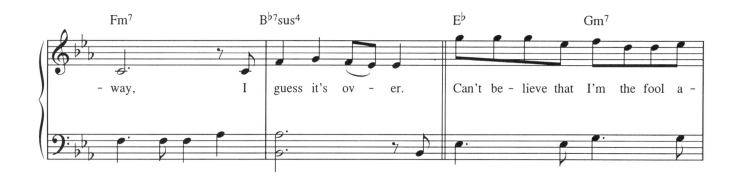

- way,   I   guess it's ov - er.   Can't be - lieve that I'm the fool a -

- gain,   I thought this love would   nev - er end.   How was I to

know?   You nev - er told___ me.   Can't be - lieve that I'm the fool a -

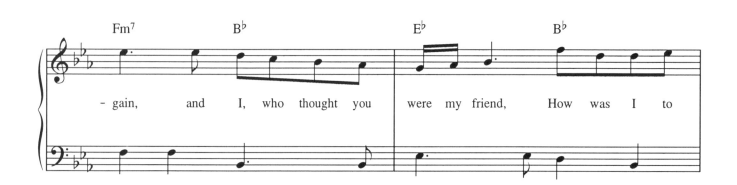

- gain,   and   I, who thought you   were my friend,   How was I to

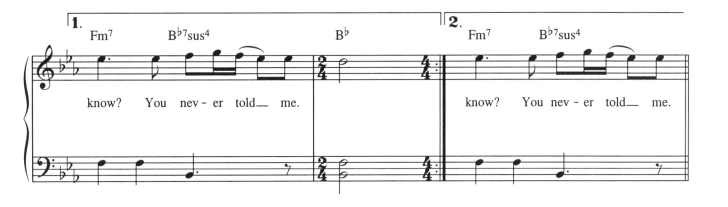

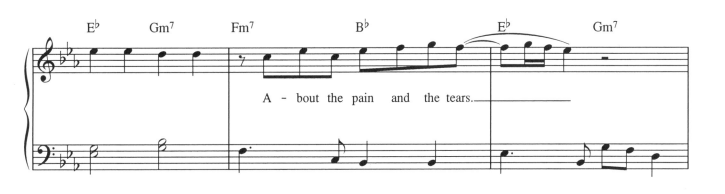

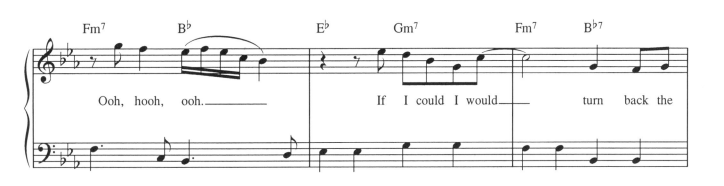

21

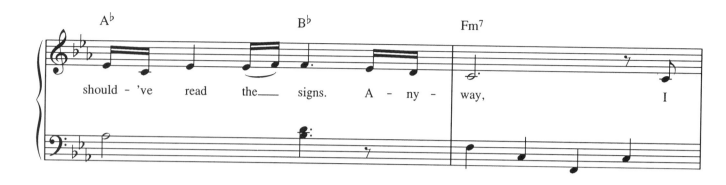

should - 've read the___ signs. A - ny - way, I

guess it's ov - er.___

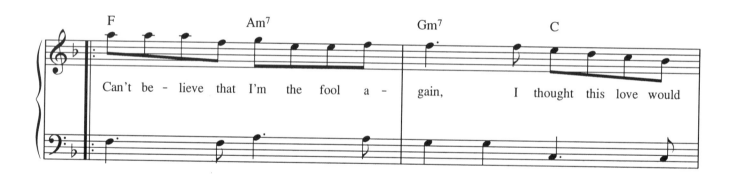

Can't be - lieve that I'm the fool a - gain, I thought this love would

nev - er end. How was I to know? You nev - er told___ me.

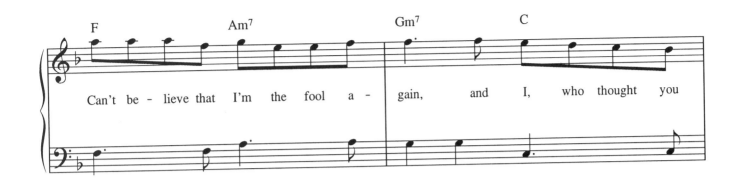

Can't be - lieve that I'm the fool a - | gain,   and   I,   who   thought   you

were my friend,   How was I to | know?   You nev - er told— me.

Verse 2:

Baby, you should've called me
When you were lonely
When you needed me to be there
Sadly, you never gave me
Too many chances
To show you how much I care.

I should've seen it coming *etc.*

Lucky

Words & Music by Max Martin, Rami Yacoub & Alexander Kronlund

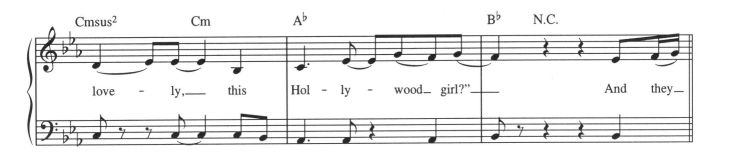

love - ly,—— this Hol - ly - wood— girl?"—— And they—

say she's so luck - y, she's a star, But she cry, cry, cries in her

lone - ly—— heart, think-ing if there's no-thing miss-ing in my life then

why—— do—— these tears—— come at night?

2. Lost in an im-age, in a dream, But there's no - one there to wake her

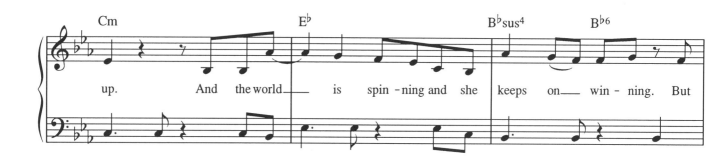

up.   And the world___ is spin -ning and she keeps on___ win - ning. But

tell me,   what hap - pens when it stops?   They go... "Is - n't___ she

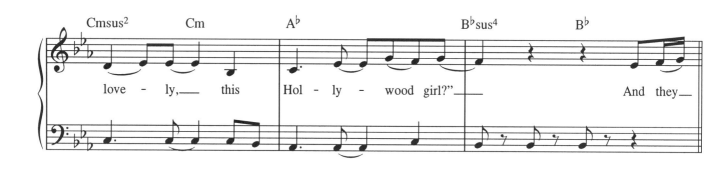

love - ly,___ this   Hol - ly - wood girl?"___   And they___

say she's so luck - y,   she's a star, But she   cry, cry, cries in her

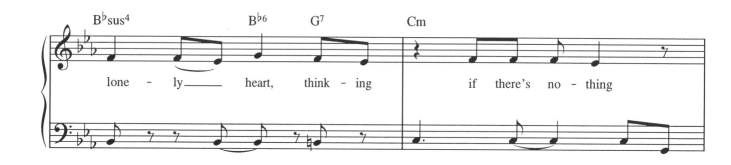

lone - ly___ heart, think - ing   if there's no - thing

miss-ing in my life then why do these tears come at night?

I, I, ah, ah, ah. "Best actress and the winner is...

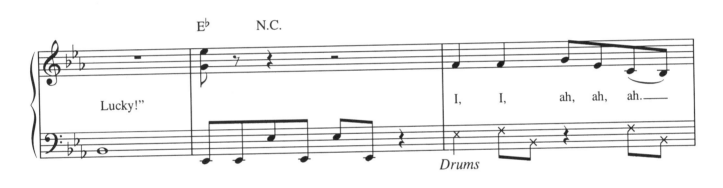

Lucky!" I, I, ah, ah, ah.

"I'm Roger Johnson for Pop News standing outside the arena waiting for Lucky!" "Is - n't she
"Oh my God, here she comes!"

love - ly, this Hol - ly - wood girl?"

27

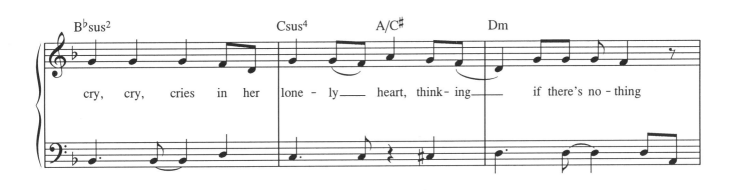

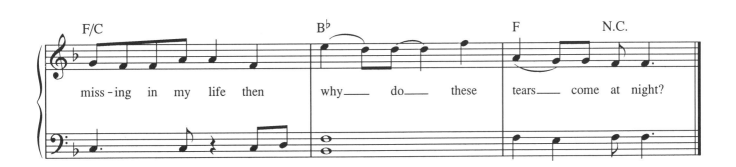

Please Forgive Me

Words & Music by David Gray

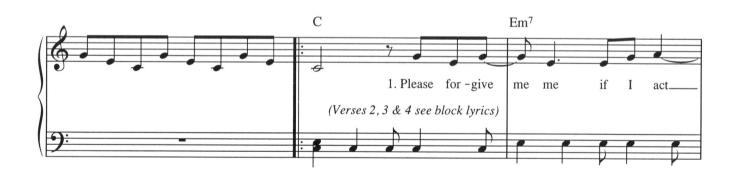

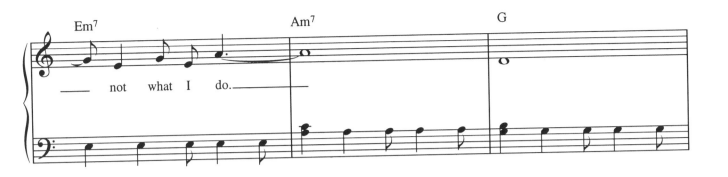

not what I do.

Feels like light - ning run - ning through my veins

ev - 'ry - time I look

at you, ev - 'ry - time

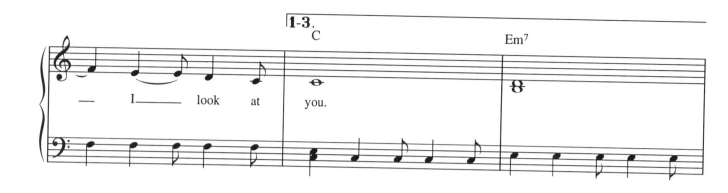

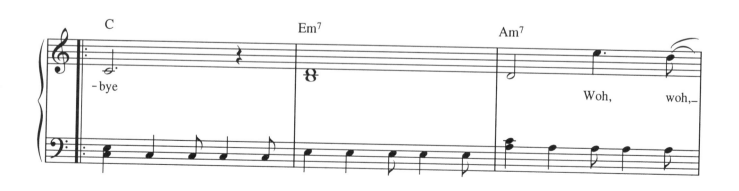

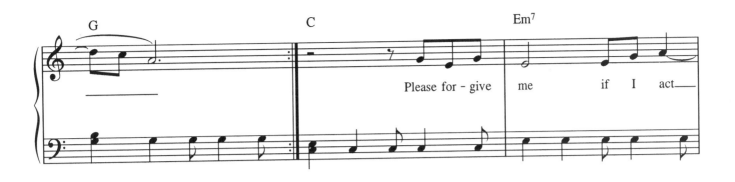

Please for - give me if I act

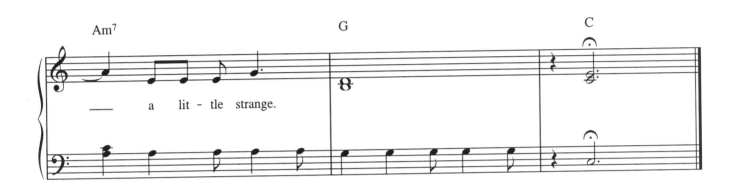

a lit - tle strange.

Verse 2:

Help me out here, all my words are falling short
And there's so much I want to say
Want to tell you just how good it feels
When you look at me that way
Ah, when you look at me that way.

Verse 3:

Throw a stone and watch the ripples flow
Moving out across the bay
Like a stone, I fall into your eyes
Deep into that mystery
Ah, deep into some mystery.

Verse 4:

I got half a mind to scream out loud
I got half a mind to die
So I won't ever have to lose you, girl
Won't ever have to say goodbye
I won't ever have to lie
Won't ever have to say goodbye.

Rise

Words & Music by Bob Dylan, Gabrielle, Ferdy Unger-Hamilton & Ollie Dagois

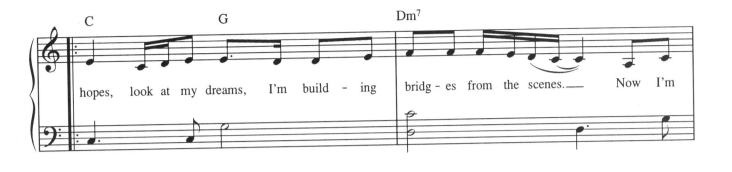

hopes, look at my dreams, I'm build - ing bridg - es from the scenes.___ Now I'm

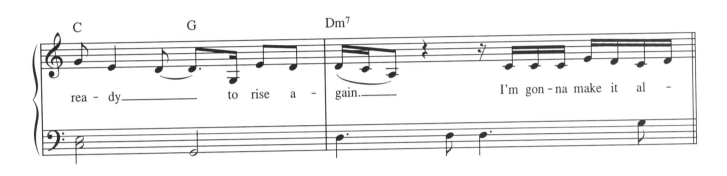

rea - dy_____ to rise a - gain.___ I'm gon - na make it al -

- right. Yes I'm gon - na rise,___ make it al - right,___ I'm___ gon - na be who I wan -na be, yeah

Repeat ad lib. to fade

ba - by. Yeah,_____ yeah.___ I'm gon -na make it al -

Verse 2:

Caught up in my thinking
Like a prisoner in my mind
You pose so many questions
That the truth is hard to find
I'd better think twice I know
That I'll get over you.

Look at my life *etc.*

Take On Me

Words & Music by Morten Harket, Mags Furuholmen & Pat Waaktaar

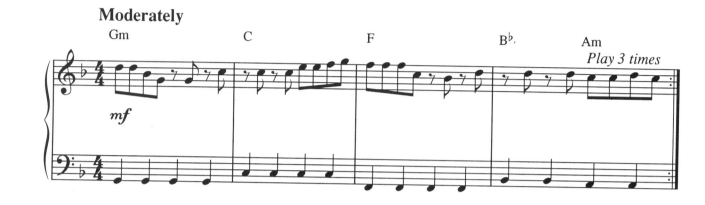

1. Talk - ing___ a - way,
(Verse 2 & 3 see block lyrics)
I don't know___ what

I'm to say. I'll say it a - ny - way.
To -

-day's a - no - ther day___ to find you___
shy - in' a - way

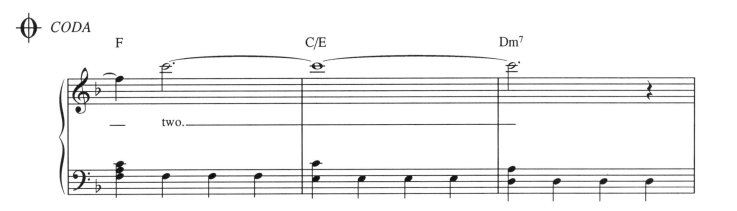

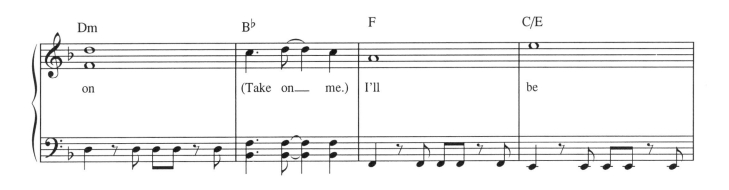

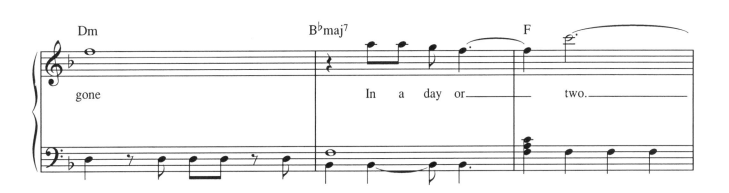

(Take on____ me.)

(Take on____ me.)

Verse 2:

So needless to say
At odds and ends
But I'll be stumbling away
Slowly learning that life is O.K.
Say after me
It's so much better to be safe than sorry.

Take on me *etc.*

Verse 3:

Oh, things that you say
Yeah, is it a life or
Just to play my worries away
You're all the things I've got to remember
You shyin' away
I'll be coming for you anyway.

Take on me *etc.*

Trouble

Words & Music by Guy Berryman, Jon Buckland, Will Champion & Chris Martin

Moderately slow

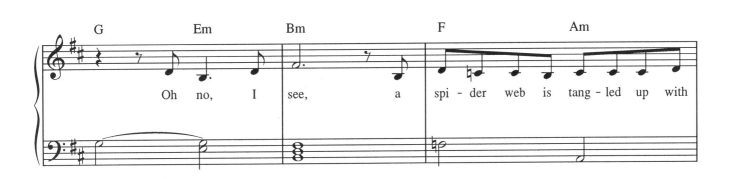

Oh no, I see, a spi - der web is tang - led up with

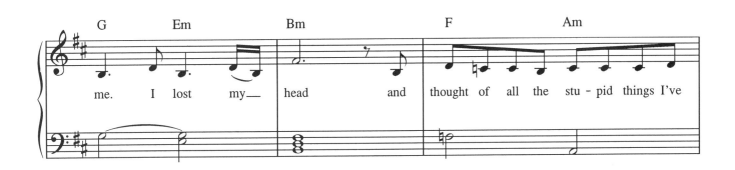

me. I lost my— head and thought of all the stu - pid things I've

said.

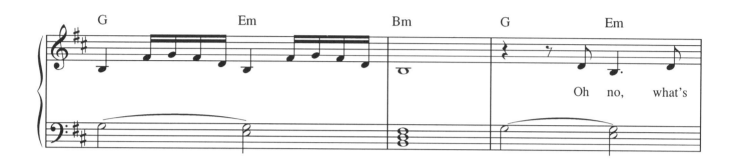

Oh no, what's

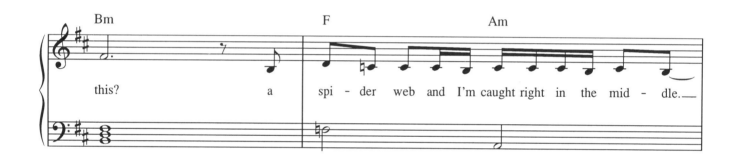

this?   a   spi - der web and I'm caught right in the mid - dle.

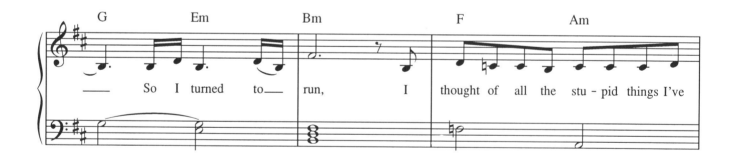

— So   I   turned   to— run,   I   thought of all the stu - pid things I've

done.   I   ne - ver meant to cause you   trou - ble,

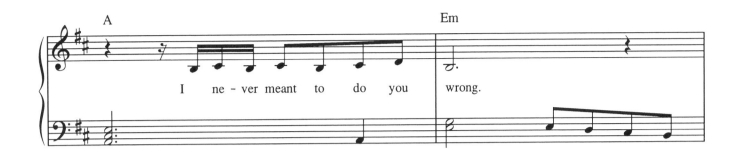

I ne-ver meant to do you wrong.

And if I ev - er caused you trou - ble Then

oh no, I ne-ver meant to do____ you harm.

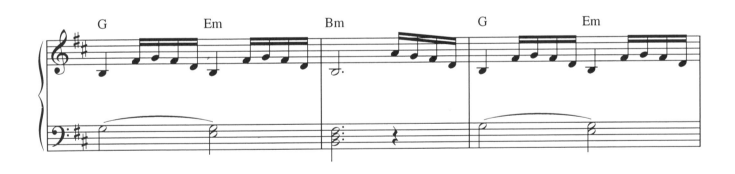

Oh no, I____ see, a

spi - der web and it's me in the mid - dle.___ So I twist and___

turn, but here am I in my lit - tle bub - ble___ Sing - ing out,

ah, I ne - ver meant to cause you trou - ble,

I ne - ver meant to do you wrong.

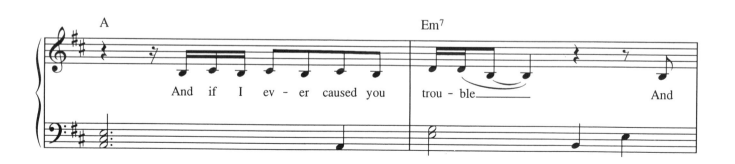

And if I ev - er caused you trou - ble___ And

ah,   no,   I   ne - ver meant to   do——— you   harm.

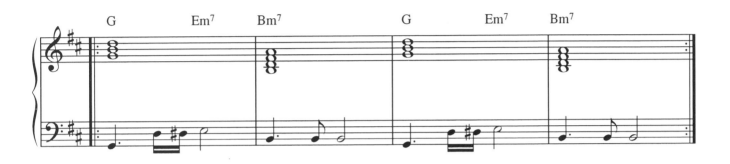

They spun   a   web   for   me,   They spun   a   web   for   me,

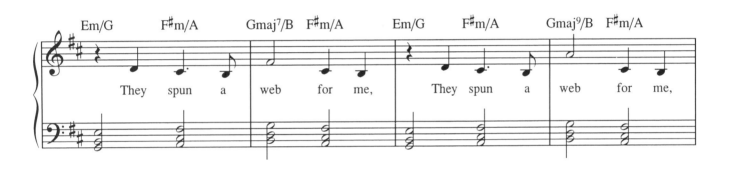

They spun   a   web   for   me...

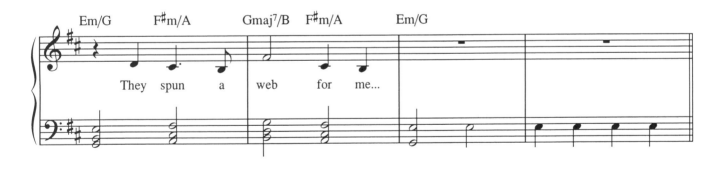

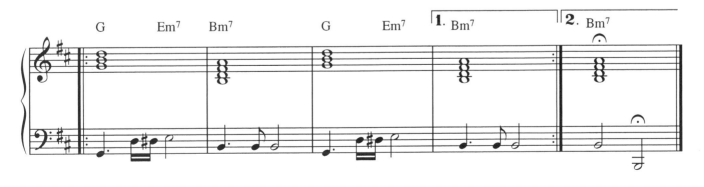